APOLOGIES

We would like to present our sincere apologies to anyc
unlikely as it may seem , find small sections of this book
therefore offensive.

We hope that by including the last cartoon, we have acheived a fair
balance between the sexes.

3

OFFICE HANKY PANKY

JOEL ROTHMAN

IDEAS UNLIMITED
PUBLISHING

This edition published in the U.K. by Ideas Unlimited (Publishing)
P.O. Box 125, Portsmouth, Hampshire PO1 4PP

© 1990 Ideas Unlimited (Publishing)

1 87196405 9   I.S.B.N.

Cover designed by Ian Churchill
Printed in Great Britain.

First published in the Netherlands by Mondria uitgevers
© 1988 Mondria uitgever en Joel Rothman
Original Title: Handbook for the
Serious Secretary

INTERNAL MEMORANDUM

DATE:

To:	From
Your Ref:	My Ref:

SUBJECT:

THE NEW COMMUNICATION PROGRAMME

I am pleased to inform you that the on going breakdown in communication within this establishment has now been resolved by a new communications programme which is guaranteed to get across even the "hard to put in words" messages.

I enclose the manual entitled "office hanky panky" and draw your attention to the message on page..........

11

18

23

- A secretary: A clever girl who can add, or a cute girl who can distract.

-A smart secretary: One who takes her shorthand at arm's length.

-An even smarter secretary: One who keeps up with her boss when he's dictating, and ahead of him when he is not.

-Did you hear about the clumsy secretary who dropped her birth control pills inside the Xerox machine? It wouldn't reproduce for a month.

-Did you hear about the absent minded executive who complained to his wife that his secretary didn't understand him.

-Did you hear about the secretary who has changed her job ten times in the past two years. But she claims she is on her last lap now.

29

30

31

44

OTHER TITLES AVAILABLE FROM IDEAS UNLIMITED (PUBLISHING).

Please send me:

- ☐ copy / copies of **"100 Chat Up Lines"** ISBN 1-871964-00-8 (128 pages A7)   @ **£1.99** (postage free)
- ☐ copy / copies of **"Of course I Love You"** ISBN 1-871964-01-6 (96 pages A6)   @ **£1.99** (postage free)
- ☐ copy / copies of **"The Beginners Guide to Kissing"** ISBN 1-871964-02-4 (64 pages A5)   @ **£2.50** (postage free)
- ☐ copy / copies of **"Tips for a Successful Marriage"** ISBN 1-871964-03-2 (64 pages A5)   @ **£2.50** (postage free)
- ☐ copy / copies of **"The Joy of Fatherhood"** ISBN 1-871964-04-0 (64 pages A5)   @ **£2.50** (postage free)
- ☐ copy / copies of **"Office Hanky Panky"** ISBN 1-871964-05-9 (64 pages A5)   @ **£2.50** (postage free)

I Have enclosed a cheque / postal order for £............................ made payable to Ideas Unlimited (Publishing)

Name: ....

Address: ....

Fill in the coupon and send it with your payment to: **Ideas Unlimited (Publishing) PO Box 125, Portsmouth PO1 4PP**